S0-CEY-784

TREES AND SHRUBS

of the

QUEEN CHARLOTTE ISLANDS

an illustrated guide

by

Sheila Douglas

Islands Ecological Research

Queen Charlotte City, British Columbia

TREES AND SHRUBS OF THE QUEEN CHARLOTTE ISLANDS

Copyright Islands Ecological Research, 1991.

Canadian Cataloguing in Publication Data

Douglas, Sheila, 1949-
Trees and Shrubs of the Queen Charlotte Islands

Includes bibliographical references and index.
ISBN 0-9695550-0-8

1. Trees--British Columbia--Queen Charlotte
Islands--Identification. 2. Shrubs--British
Columbia--Queen Charlotte Islands--Identification.
3. Botany--British Columbia--Queen Charlotte
Islands. I. Islands Ecological Research. II.
Title.
QK203.B7D68 1991   582.160971112   C91-091714-0

Published by Islands Ecological Research, Box 970,

Queen Charlotte City, British Columbia, Canada.

PREFACE

The reputation of the Queen Charlotte Islands as the "Galapagos of the North" has generated a multitude of studies on the Islands' plant and animal life. Everything from black bears and whales to less conspicuous forms of life such as beetles, mosses and algae have become subjects of scientific reports. Yet often these studies are inaccessible to a large group of people whose expertise consists of broad enthusiasm and curiosity about the Islands' natural life.

The need for a guide to the common plants of the Queen Charlotte Islands impressed Charles Gee of Masset, who asked if I would be interested in doing a series of drawings of tree species of the Islands. The project quickly grew to include all the woody plants - over 50 species of conifers and flowering plants, encompassing most of the conspicuous vegetation on the Islands.

As I worked on the drawings and laboured through the descriptions, I found that I could not quite answer my own question "Who is this book for? the professional botanist? the naturalist? the tourist?" Near completion of the project, I realized that I was preparing the field guide I had looked for 10 years previously when I first began my botanical explorations of the Islands. As a neophyte in science, I wanted pictures, common names and lots of description. I wanted some clues about the structure of the plants and science of naming and describing them. And I wanted some story, some spark of what this plant was, why it grew where it did, and how it fit into the living systems I saw on the Islands and on the northwest coast.

Using *Flora of the Queen Charlotte Islands* by J.A. Calder and R. L. Taylor, Nancy Turner's *Food Plants of British Columbia Indians* and Lewis Clark's splendid *Wildflowers of British Columbia*, I came to know the vegetation. What started as putting names to plants became a serious study in pollination systems. It took many diversions, including earning a formal education in botany, before that initial idea - an accessible, informative identification guide - flowered, resulting in the completion of this book.

Although it may not fulfil all the demands of a fledgling botanist, I trust it will be a companion in the pleasure of discovery.

I would like to thank Tom Reimchen, who offered support throughout the project, and to Charles Gee, for the initial impetus and funding for the book. My thanks go to Bob and Fern Henderson, John and Jennifer Davies, Margo Hearne and Bristol Foster for their continued interest. I am grateful to Hans Roemer and Vicki Bragan for editorial assistance.

Sheila Douglas
Drizzle Lake, Queen Charlotte Islands
22 June 1989

CONTENTS

INTRODUCTION

More than ten thousand years ago, the Queen Charlotte Islands were locked in ice, like the rest of Canada buried under the deep crust of a glacier. Ice-free patches of land persisted through the cold, probably harbouring life from an earlier warmer era. Refuges may have been large enough for a complex community of plants, insects, fish and small mammals. At the least, there were pockets of soil that supported a few hardy alpine herbs and mosses.

Over time the hemisphere warmed again, the glaciers retreated, and at the edge of the shrinking ice-cap colonization of the ice-scarred land began. Plants that survived in the refuges recolonized their habitats quickly. Wind-borne seeds from the south and east, and later, seeds carried across the Hecate Strait on the feet and in the bellies of birds sprouted and grew. Coastal landslides on the mainland may have released whole hillsides of vegetation into the ocean which rafted across the Hecate Strait, bringing with them mini-ecosystems of plants and animals.

At some time, the Hecate Strait shallowed and a land bridge stretched most of the way to mainland British Columbia, allowing immigrant plant communities to move across to the Islands. Many plants failed to make the crossing. Others arrived on the Islands but went extinct. Plants were not alone in colonizing the Islands. Insects, mammals and birds followed the rich food source - browsing the vegetation, feeding on seeds, fruits and leaves, boring into stems and dead wood, eating pollen, nectar and sap.

As communities of plants and animals developed, they were moulded by the unique character of the Islands. Surrounded by water, it is not surprising that the ocean, and the climate it engenders, has had such an effect on the Islands. The ridge of mountains along the west coast is a barrier lifting and catching the air-borne water drifting in from the Pacific. The Pacific "rain forest" is aptly named, since the forests depend on the mist, rain and soil moisture for their life. Ample rainfall also feeds the

1

bog habitats, creating a unique environment over poorly drained terrain. And the shorn, wind-shaped thickets of coastal salal and cedar attest to the fact that the Queen Charlotte Islands weather some of the fiercest winds in coastal Canada. Yet these extremes are moderated by the vast heat-sink of the surrounding ocean, warming the winters and cooling the summers.

The plants of the Queen Charlotte Islands - isolated from the mainland, sharing a mist-shrouded and volatile environment and possessed of an ancient botanical legacy - developed into communities as unique as the forces that shaped them.

TREES AND SHRUBS

Plants with a tough outer layer of bark and a woody stem or trunk are grouped together as trees and shrubs. The two groups are distinguished from each other by nothing more sophisticated than size and shape: a Sitka Spruce is a tree because it is large and has a single trunk and Salal is a shrub because it is relatively small with multiple stems. But what spruce and salal share, what makes them both woody plants with a common developmental strategy, is their growth pattern. The growing part of the plant - the cambium - located just under the bark, produces a new layer of tissue each year, resulting in an accumulated increase in girth. What we call wood, in spruce or in salal, is this accumulated plant tissue, each year marked off by a growth ring.

The structural strength of wood gives trees and shrubs a height advantage over herbaceous plants (those whose stems and foliage die back each year). A plant that can overtop its neighbours wins in the competition for sunlight. Large girth and buttressing bases make wide-spreading branches possible, to capture sunlight and to attract pollinators and disperse seeds. Once established in a favourable, stable habitat, trees and shrubs may reach great size and great age, successfully producing offspring year after year.

2

CONIFERS AND FLOWERING PLANTS

Woody plants can be found in both of the two major plant lineages - gymnosperms, which includes the conifers, and angiosperms, the flowering plants. The obvious and most significant distinction between the two groups is that the reproductive parts in conifers are borne in cones (for example, Sitka Spruce and Red Cedar) while in flowering plants, reproductive parts are contained in flowers (Pacific Crab Apple and Salal). The seeds of conifers have no protective layers of tissue surrounding them (*gymno* means naked, *sperm* is seed) while seeds of flowering plants are protected from desiccation and predation by an enclosing carpel (*angio* means vessel).

Most conifers are evergreen, with needle-like leaves (as in Western Hemlock) or scale-like leaves (as in Red Cedar) that persist on the tree for several years. Male cones, which are clustered near the ends of branches, produce a prodigious amount of pollen which is transported away by wind. Female cones grow singly near or at the tips of branches, on different branches of the same tree or on different trees than male cones. Pollen lands on the open scales of the small, undeveloped female cone; the scales close up, sealing the cone while the seeds are fertilized and the cone matures. When the cone opens again, up to 2 years after pollination, the mature winged seeds are released and dispersed by the wind.

Flowering plants are more flexible in life-style than conifers. They have an enormous variety of size and form of foliage and flowers; they can be woody or herbaceous, and deciduous or evergreen. Their reproductive cycle is relatively short and, in some cases, can be completed in a matter of days. In flowering plants, pollen is produced in anthers, immature seeds are protected by an enclosing carpel, and both male and female structures are surrounded by usually conspicuous petals. The colour, shape and smell of flowers attract insects or birds; while gathering nectar from a series of flowers, they transport pollen to carpels. After fertilization, the flower parts die and the carpel develops into a protective covering while the seeds mature. When ripe, seeds are dispersed by wind, water or animals. In many of the woody flowering plants, the carpel develops into a colourful fruit; birds and mammals, in the process of eating the fruit and defecating, effectively disperse the seeds.

Conifers evolved over 200 million years ago and once dominated the land. They are slow-growing, usually massive, with a ponderously slow reproductive cycle. In contrast, flowering plants, with a more recent evolutionary history, are the upstarts of the plant world. Their characteristics of rapid growth, rapid reproduction and flexibility in form and life-style have allowed them to come to dominate the world vegetation.

PLANT COMMUNITIES ON THE QUEEN CHARLOTTE ISLANDS

Forest

The exposed coastline of the Queen Charlotte Islands is dominated by Sitka Spruce (*Picea sitchensis*) forest. The tree not only survives the buffeting winds but actually thrives in the habitat, obtaining nutrients from the salt spray. Its high nutrient requirements are also met in the rich soils of river floodplains.

Western Red Cedar (*Thuja plicata*) and Western Hemlock (*Tsuga heterophylla*), intolerant of ocean spray, make up about 90% of the interior forests on the Islands. Western Hemlock, with its high shade tolerance and ability to grow optimally on the poorest and most acidic soils, dominates. Western Red Cedar, equally shade tolerant but requiring pockets of more nutritious soil is second in abundance.

The largest trees, and especially the massive Sitka Spruce for which the Islands are famous, grow on the floodplains of large rivers. Red Alder (*Alnus rubra*) and Sitka Alder (*A. viridis* ssp. *sinuata*) are found here as well, usually on banks and gravel bars.

The understorey of shrubs can be sparse to thicket-like,

4

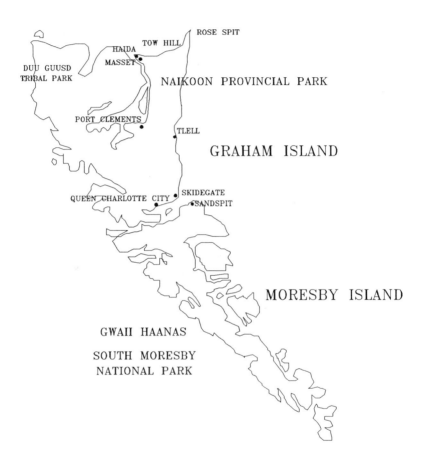

ROSE SPIT

TOW HILL

HAIDA
MASSET

DUU GUUSD
TRIBAL PARK

NAIKOON PROVINCIAL PARK

PORT CLEMENTS

TLELL

GRAHAM ISLAND

QUEEN CHARLOTTE CITY

SKIDEGATE
SANDSPIT

MORESBY ISLAND

GWAII HAANAS

SOUTH MORESBY
NATIONAL PARK

QUEEN CHARLOTTE ISLANDS
HAIDA GWAII

depending on the amount of light that filters through the canopy. Salal (*Gaultheria shallon*), Red Huckleberry (*Vaccinium parvifolium*) and Rusty Pacific Menziesia (*Menziesia ferruginea*) are ubiquitous, but will vary in abundance under different light conditions. Stink Currant (*Ribes bracteosum*), Salmonberry (*Rubus spectabilis*) and Blue Huckleberry (*Vaccinium alaskaense* and *V. ovalifolium*) grow in more nutrient-rich patches in the forest.

Gwaii Haanas (South Moresby National Park Reserve) contains the full range of forest types: protected east coast islets have abundant Western Red Cedar, exposed west coast bays are fringed with Sitka Spruce and low-lying land is covered in Western Hemlock and Western Red Cedar forest.

Easily accessible examples of the Islands' forest communities are in Naikoon Provincial Park, Graham Island. The road to Tow Hill follows ancient stabilized dunes, with Sitka Spruce growing on the beach margin and moss-laden Western Hemlock and Western Red Cedar forest protected from the severest ocean elements inland. A hike from Tow Hill to Rose Spit and south along the east coast to Tlell traverses along some impressive dune forest communities. South of Tlell, all along the east coast of Graham Island, Sitka Spruce forest community dominates, growing on the margin of rocky and shingle beaches.

Coastal rock

Woody plants are plentiful, often luxuriant, beyond the reach of ocean spray on coastal rock and cliff communities. Nootka Rose (*Rosa nutkana*), Pacific Crab Apple (*Malus fusca*), Common Snowberry (*Symphoricarpos albus*), Red Huckleberry (*Vaccinium parvifolium*) and Copperbush (*Cladothamnus pyroliflorus*) are common in the habitat. Coastal rock communities flourish along the exposed east coast of Moresby Island. Rock promontories and islets in Skidegate Inlet are also prime areas for these species.

Bog

The Islands' bogs (called simply 'muskeg' locally) nurture a number of woody plant species. Adapted to windy, natur-

6

ally acidic and nutrient-poor conditions, they are usually prostrate, dwarfed or diminutive. Lodgepole Pine (*Pinus contorta*), usually in "bonsai" form, is the most common tree on the open bog along with low-growing Yellow Cedar (*Chamaecyparis nootkatensis*) and Common Juniper (*Juniperus communis*). Black Crowberry (*Empetrum nigrum*), Western Swamp Kalmia (*Kalmia microphylla* ssp. *occidentalis*), Bog Rosemary (*Andromeda polifolia*), Labrador Tea (*Ledum palustre*), Bog Cranberry (*Vaccinium oxycoccus*) and many other members of the Heath Family (Ericaceae) are abundant. Most lowland bogs have a thick mat of spongy *Sphagnum* (peat) moss as a ground cover and are called "raised bogs". In subalpine habitats and at lower elevations on the west coast, bogs have a thin or broken layer of moss and sedges with outcrops of underlying rock. These "blanket bogs" contain additional, sub-alpine species such as Club-moss Cassiope (*Cassiope lycopodioides* ssp. *cristapilosa*). Red and Yellow Cedar and Western Hemlock in the subalpine are often dwarfed and wind-sheared, forming impenetrable thickets.

Bogs are ubiquitous on northern Graham Island. The interior of Naikoon Provincial Park is a patchwork of bogs, lakes and Western Hemlock/Red Cedar forest. Open *Sphagnum* bog are found at intervals along the road from Masset to Port Clements. At low elevations on the exposed west coast of both Graham and Moresby Islands, blanket bog and sub-alpine communities are found; more accessible are those on the east coast in Gwaii Haanas, usually above 200 meters, where blanket bog and subalpine grade into each other.

Alpine and subalpine

The slopes and peaks of the west coast mountains sequester rare and endemic plants of the Queen Charlotte Islands. The endemic shrub, Net-veined Dwarf Willow (*Salix reticulata* ssp. *glabellicarpa*) grows in this mist-shrouded habitat. Restricted to mountain habitats (but not unique to the Islands) are Merten's Cassiope (*Cassiope mertensiana*), Steller's Cassiope (*Cassiope stelleriana*) and Cream Mountain-heather (*Phyllodoce glanduliflora*), which can form a dense and continuous ground cover. The alpine heath plants, with a bonus of endemic herbs, are a treasure for

7

the hiker, since they are never found in areas with road access and are rarely found at elevations less than 500 meters. Slatechuck Mountain (locally named Sleeping Beauty), west of Queen Charlotte City, is the most easily accessible alpine area. The San Cristoval Mountain chain on Moresby Island and the peaks of southwest Graham Island are the remote and cloud-crowned havens for these plants.

HAIDA USE OF WOODY PLANTS

Thousands of years before a botanist gave the name *Gaultheria shallon* to the ubiquitous salal, the Haida people knew it intimately as a bounteous provider of fruit, one of the hundreds of plants used for food, medicine and the implements of day-to-day living on Haida Gwaii. Among the shrubs, the most important traditional plant foods are the fruits of woody plants such as Salal, Red and Blue Huckleberry (*Vaccinium parvifolium, V. alask-aense, V. ovalifolium*), Salmonberry (*Rubus spectabilis*), Thimbleberry (*Rubus parviflorus*), Pacific Crab Apple (*Malus fusca*), Nootka Rose (*Rosa nutkana*), Bog and Moun-tain Cranberry (*Vaccinium oxycoccus, V. vitis-idaea*) and Pacific Saskatoon (*Amelanchier alnifolia* ssp. *semi-integrifolia*). Some fruits are eaten fresh, but, trad-itionally, most were prepared and stored, dried in cakes or immersed in water for later use, to be mixed with salmon eggs, eulachon grease, or eaten as is. The Haida avoid the inedible berries of Devil's Club (*Oplopanax horridus*), Twinberry Honeysuckle (*Lonicera involucrata*) and Snowberry (*Symphoricarpos albus*), as do most other northwest coast people.

Almost all of the tree species, Red Cedar, Yellow Cedar, Western Hemlock, Sitka Spruce, Western Yew and Red and Sitka Alder, were used to carve tools and utensils; shrubs such as Scouler's Willow (*Salix scouleriana*), Red-osier Dogwood (*Cornus sericea* ssp. *occidentalis*), and Snowberry (*Symphoricarpos albus*) were used casually for drying racks and for frames for food preparation or temporary shelter. But the tree that surpasses all in its importance, for both the livelihood and culture of the Haida, is the

Western Red Cedar. It provides the basic material for posts, planks and roofing for traditional longhouses, for totem poles, canoes, boxes and baskets and, historically, mortuary poles, clothing, fish-nets and implements for hunting, fishing, food gathering and eating.

CONSERVATION

In Gwaii Haanas (South Moresby National Park), Naikoon Provincial Park and the V. J. Krajina Ecological Reserve (Port Chanal), representative areas of most of the lowland plant communities are conserved. Addition of Duu Guusd Tribal Park on northwest Graham Island, the headwaters of the Tlell River and alpine plant habitat such as the area around Takakia Lake would insure some integrity of woody plant communities on the Queen Charlotte Islands. But for the river valley forests - the true giants of the Islands' conifers - it is already too late. Most of the forests along the Yakoun, Mamin, Copper, Deena and Naden Rivers have been cut or are slated for cut in the near future; with a period of less than 70 years between each sub-sequent cut, we will never see trees of that age and size, nor their natural communities again.

Conservationists and foresters are now realizing that old growth forest is a much more complex and diverse habitat than previously thought. Although many of the character-istics of old growth have been formally defined, for example, the presence of dead standing snags, of fallen trees that act as nurse logs for seedlings, of a range in tree ages and sizes, the critical research on biodiversity and on ecological relationships has not been done. Issues such as nutrient cycling, critical patch size, endangered species habitat and invertebrate diversity have not been addressed. For most forest types, the simple task of counting, naming and documenting the plants and animals has not even begun.

PLANT IDENTIFICATION

All trees and shrubs native to the Queen Charlotte Islands are included in this guide; 36 common species are illustrated and described, while the remaining 19, which are unlikely to be encountered, are described with the species they most closely resemble. Several conspicuous non-native shrubs are described, but those restricted to yards and towns are omitted. Woody species account for 10% of the approximately 600 native and introduced vascular plants on the Islands. Flowering herbs are the most diverse group on the Charlottes, making up 50% of the flora; the remaining 40% are grasses, sedges and ferns and their allies. Yet the woody plants are the most conspicuous part of the Islands' vegetation and make up about 90% of its biomass.

Tree silhouettes of conifers (included with the species description), and leaf outlines of flowering plants (on the following pages) can be used for initial identification. Variation is often rampant within a species, especially in leaves of flowering plants, depending on soils, the amount of light and age. As such, live specimens will not always conform to the tree silhouette or to the leaf outline given.

Both common and scientific names are included in the plant description. Common names are often applicable only locally. There may be several common names for the same plant (for example, *Symphoricarpos albus* is called both Snowberry and Waxberry) and 2 different plants may have the same common name (for example, Blue Huckleberry may mean *Vaccinium alaskaense* or *Vaccinium ovalifolium*). In contrast, the scientific name, or binomial (= two names), consisting of genus and species (*Gaultheria shallon*), is

a. **Pacific Saskatoon**, *Amelanchier alnifolia* (78); b. **Black Hawthorn**, *Crataegus douglasii* (79); c. **Pacific Crab Apple**, *Malus fusca* (80); d. **Scotch Broom**, *Cytisus scoparius* (72); e. **Nootka Rose**, *Rosa nutkana*, (82); f. **Sitka Mountain Ash**, *Sorbus sitchensis* ssp. *sitchensis* (40). All leaves are shown actual size.

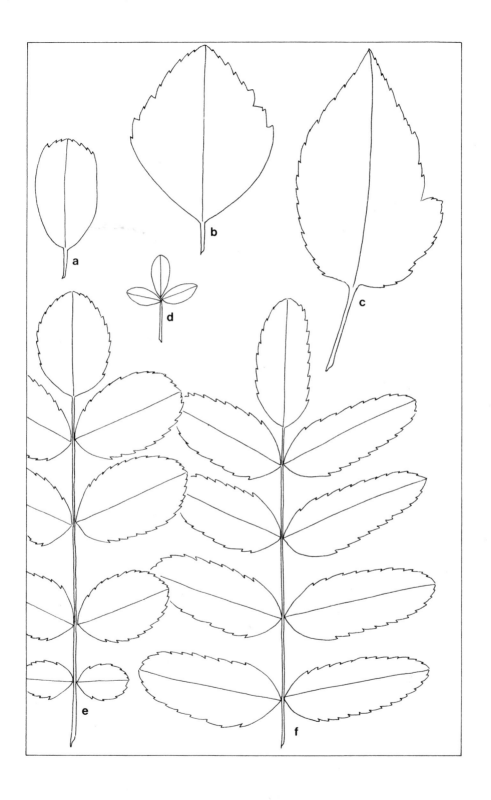

unique to the species and in all parts of the world, refers to the same plant. The binomial is followed by the names of the botanists who described and classified the plant; this is called the authority (*Gaultheria shallon* Pursh) and including it removes any doubt as to which plant it is. In this guide, the standard for scientific and common names is *Vascular Plants of British Columbia* and *Flora of the Queen Charlotte Islands*.

Plant species that have common characteristics, reflecting their evolutionary history, are grouped into families which have both common and scientific names (the Heath Family is Ericaceae, the Rose Family is Rosaceae). In the following pages, families are arranged alphabetically.

Although this is primarily an identification guide, I have tried to indicate briefly some of the plants' natural history and to touch on historical and present-day uses of plants. For those who want to pursue these botanical paths, there is a wealth of information in the source books that are listed at the end of the guide.

a. **Bog Rosemary**, *Andromeda polifolia* (46); b. **Kinnikinnick**, *Arctostaphylos uva-ursi* (70); c. **Crowberry**, *Empetrum nigrum* (44); d. **Club-moss Cassiope**, *Cassiope lycopodioides* ssp. *cristapilosa* (48); e. **Merten's Cassiope**, *C. mertensiana* (48); f. **Steller's Cassiope**, *C. stelleriana* (50); g. **Copperbush**, *Cladothamnus pyroliflorus* (51); h. **Swamp Laurel**, *Kalmia microphylla* ssp. *occidentalis* (54); i. **Labrador Tea**, *Ledum groenlandicum* (56); j. **Alpine-azalea**, *Loiseleuria procumbens* (46); k. **Rusty Pacific Menziesia**, *Menziesia ferruginea* (58); l. **Cream Mountain-Heather**, *Phyllodoce glanduliflora* (50); m. **Dwarf Blueberry**, *Vaccinium caespitosum* (63); n. **Bog Cranberry**, *V. oxycoccus* (64); o. **Bog Blueberry**, *V. uliginosum* (68); p. **Mountain Cranberry**, *V. vitis-idaea* ssp. *minus* (70); q. **Salal**, *Gaultheria shallon* (52); r. **Oval-leaved Blueberry**, *V. ovalifolium* (62); s. **Red Huckleberry**, *V. parvifolium* (66); t. **Alaskan Blueberry**, *Vaccinium alaskaense* (60); u. **Sweet Gale**, *Myrica gale* (78); v. **Snowberry**, *Symphoricarpos albus* (42). All leaves are shown actual size.

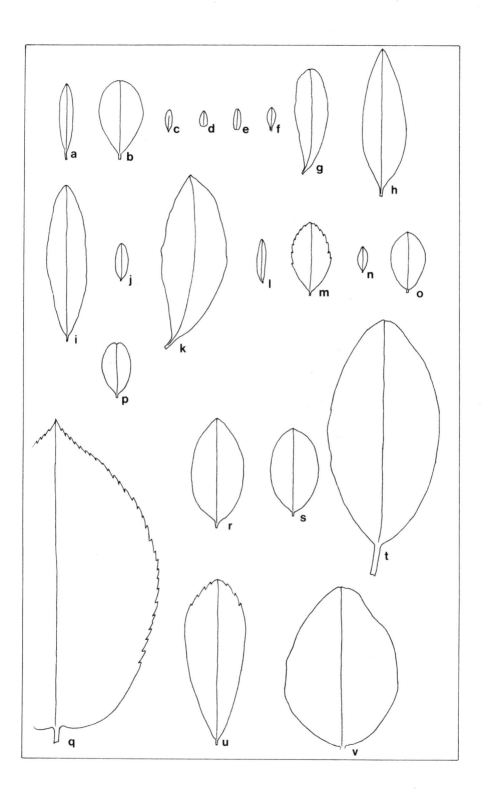

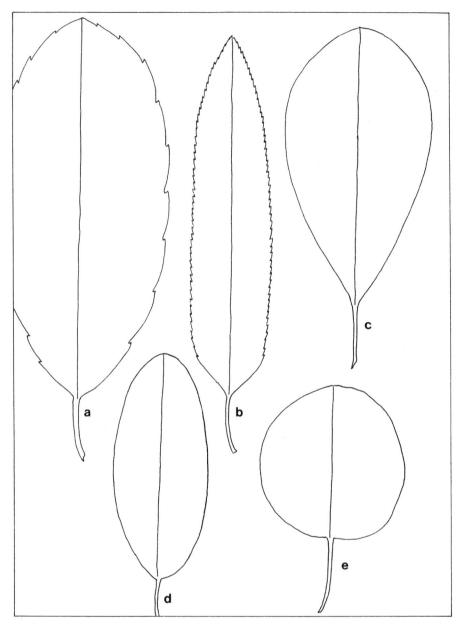

a. **Hooker's Willow**, *Salix hookeriana* (88); b. **Pacific Willow**, *S. lasiandra* (90); c. **Scouler's Willow**, *S. scouleriana* (88); d. **Sitka Willow**, *S. sitchensis* (90); e. **Net-leaved Dwarf Willow**, *S. reticulata* ssp. *glabellicarpa* (90). All leaves are shown actual size.

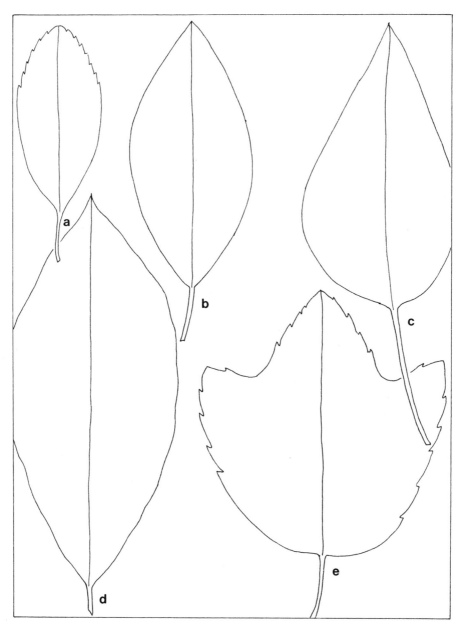

a. **Hardhack,** *Spirea douglasii* (88); b. **Red-osier Dogwood,** *Cornus sericea* (44); c. **Black Cottonwood,** *Populus balsamifera* (90); d. **Twinberry Honeysuckle,** *Lonicera involucrata* (38); e. **High Bush Cranberry,** *Viburnum edule* (42). All leaves are shown actual size.

a. **Stink Currant**, *Ribes bracteosum* (74); b. **Trailing Black Currant**, *R.laxiflorum* (76); c. **Black Swamp Gooseberry**, *R. lacustre* (76); d. **Red Alder**, *Alnus rubra* (36); e. **Sitka Alder**, *A. viridis* (36); f. **Western Thimbleberry**, *Rubus parviflorus* (84); g. **Devil's-Club**, *Oplopanax horridus* (34); h. **Salmonberry**, *Rubus spectabilis* (86); i. **Coastal Red Elder**, *Sambucus racemosa* (40). All leaves are shown 3/5 actual size.

TREES AND SHRUBS OF THE QUEEN CHARLOTTE ISLANDS

CONIFERS

CUPRESSACEAE   CYPRESS FAMILY

Chamaecyparis nootkatensis (D. Don) Spach   **Yellow Cedar**

Yellow Cedar, growing to a maximum of 20 m in height on the Islands, has a conical to pyramidal profile and in old trees, a buttressed trunk. The foliage on the main branches hangs vertically and parallel, giving the whole tree a drooping appearance. The bark is greyish-brown and thin, growing in vertical stringy ridges. The wood itself is pale yellow in colour, close-grained, strong and aromatic when freshly split. The bluish-green leaves are small overlapping scales that are usually tightly pressed to the stem; in some branchlets, the scales may flare out. The arrangement of the scales makes the branchlets squarish in cross section. The young leaves have a pungent odour. Cones are spherical, 10 mm in diameter, with 6 or fewer woody mushroom-shaped scales radiating from the cone axis. The mature seeds are released from the cones during the first or second autumn after pollination.

Yellow Cedar is distributed throughout the Islands, but is uncommon and never forms continuous stands. At low elevations, it grows along lakeshores and in bogs, but its domain is the subalpine forest. In wind-exposed habitats, it is reduced to a densely-branched shrub. The tree grows along the Pacific coast from Oregon to the Gulf of Alaska.

Although less common and less versatile than Red Cedar, Yellow Cedar has a light-coloured, pliable inner bark that was used by the Haida for weaving baskets and clothing. The straight-grained, strong wood was used for implements like handles and paddles and for eating utensils.

Key characteristics: Drooping branches with branchlets hanging vertically; leaves scale-like, bluish-green, stems not flattened; pungent smell of foliage and wood; cones spherical, of 6 scales.

18

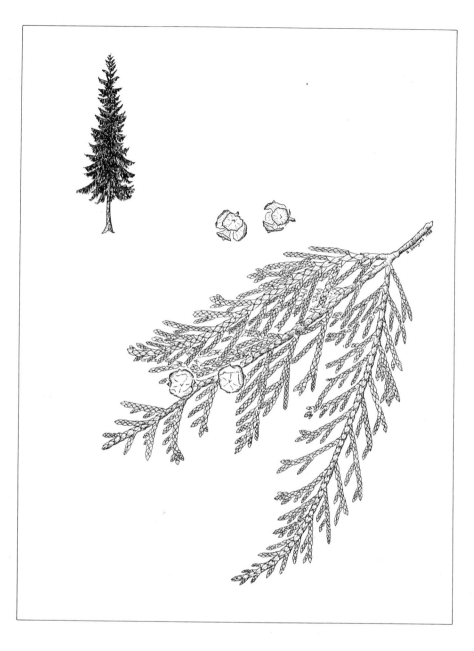

Yellow cedar, *Chamaecyparis nootkatensis*. (X 3/5)

19

CUPRESSACEAE   CYPRESS FAMILY

Juniperus communis L.   **Common Juniper**

Common Juniper is a prostrate shrub with stiff spreading
branches that grows up to half a meter tall. The leaves
are needle-like, up to 13 mm long, with hard sharp points;
they are angled upwards in whorls of three around the
stem. The needles appear upside-down, with the upper
surface white and rolled in at the edges and the lower
surface lustrous green. The male and female cones are on
different plants. The female cone is berry-like, about
8 mm in diameter, ripening from pale green in its first
year to bluish-black the following summer. The Juniper
"berry" is formed from 3 fleshy scales fused around the
seed.

Juniper is distributed throughout the Islands in lowland
bogs and subalpine habitats. It grows all across North
America.

The berry-like cones are edible, but were not eaten historically, neither are they picked today on the Islands.
Blue Grouse and Deer Mice eat and disperse the seeds.

Key characteristics: Prostrate conifer with sharp
needle-like leaves; cones berry-like, spherical, dusty
bluish-black.

Common Juniper, *Juniperus communis*. (X 1/2)

Thuja plicata D. Don   **Western Red Cedar**

Western Red Cedar has a narrow conical crown of foliage
with curved J-shaped branches; the branchlets form horizontal or diagonal sprays. The trunk is often flared and
lobed at the base. On the Islands, the tree may be up to
30 m tall. The fibrous bark is reddish-brown to grey,
ridged vertically such that it tears off in long strips.
The wood is straight-grained, very light and reddish in
colour, turning silvery-grey after years of exposure to
light. The leaves are small, overlapping scales tightly
pressed against the stem, giving the appearance of a flat
braid. Cones are 1 to 1.5 cm long and erect on the
branches; they consist of a few woody, over-lapping scales
that open to release winged seeds in their first season.

Red Cedar is abundant on the Islands, growing in lowland
forests with Western Hemlock, on the coast in protected
inlets and in a small tree or dwarf form in lowland and
subalpine bogs. It grows only in western North America,
from California to Alaska. On the Islands, regeneration of
Red Cedar is low in both natural habitats and logged-over
areas due to browsing by introduced Blacktail Deer.

Wood that is light, straight-grained for easy splitting,
soft for carving and decay resistant make Red Cedar the
most useful and cherished tree on the coast. Traditionally, Red Cedar provided the Haida with the raw material
for shelter, clothing, transportation, fuel, utensils,
tools, ceremony and art. Whole trees were worked into
canoes and totem poles. Wood planks split from standing
trees were the construction material for long houses. The
pliable inner bark was stripped, processed and woven into
clothing, baskets and mats. Carved Red Cedar provided implements for fishing and for gathering, storing and eating
food. There is no plant that has had such a monumental
impact on survival and culture of the Islands' people.

Key characteristics: J-shaped branches with branchlets
spreading diagonally; blue-tinged scale-like needles;
cones with a few overlapping woody scales.

Western Red Cedar, *Thuja plicata*. (X 3/5)

Picea sitchensis (Bong.) Carr.   **Sitka Spruce**

Sitka Spruce is the largest conifer on the Queen Charlotte Islands - old giants can reach heights of 75 m. The base is often buttressed, but the trunk is characteristically cylindrical with little decrease in diameter over much of it height. The bark is thin, grey to brown and distinctly scaly. The long stiff branches are angled upwards near the apex of the tree; lower branches arch downwards, usually with the ends curving slightly upwards. The leaves are flattened needles about 2.5 cm long, with stiff sharp tips. They are spreading and spirally arranged on the stems. The pendant cones are up to 10 cm long; they have numerous apically toothed scales that are pale brown and papery. Cones are shed when the seeds are mature, during their first autumn.

Sitka Spruce is a common tree along the fringe of coast exposed to salt spray and wind, such as the east coast of Graham Island, where it reaches heights of 20 m. Its greatest development is in well-drained terrain bordering the major rivers on Graham and Moresby Islands. It is distributed throughout the Islands in the appropriate habitat. Its world distribution is a thin coastal strip running from California to Alaska.

The roots of Sitka Spruce were finely woven into baskets and hats by the Haida. Many exquisite spruce root articles are still made today. The sticky pungent pitch is widely used on the Islands, today as in the past, as an effective poultice for infections and wounds.

Key characteristics: Straight, cylindrical trunk with thin scaly bark; needles radiating from all sides of the branches, prickly sharp; long cones with thin toothed scales.

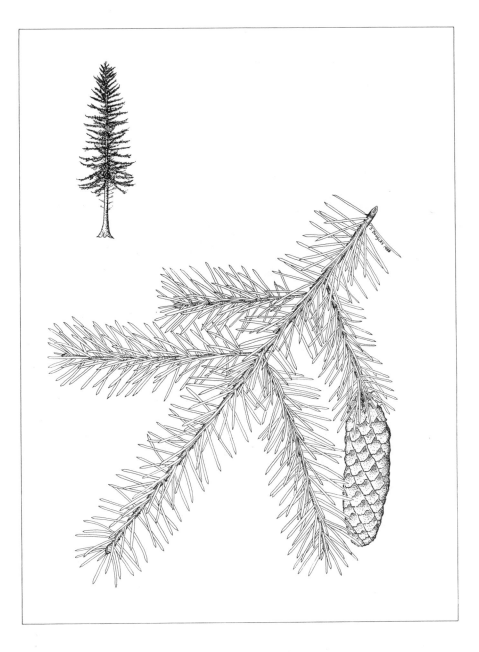

Sitka Spruce, *Picea sitchensis.* (X 3/5)

Pinus contorta Dougl. ex Loud.   **Lodgepole Pine**

Lodgepole Pine varies in size and shape depending on the conditions under which it grows. In bog and subalpine habitats, the tree is dwarf - a "bonsai" of 1 to 2 m in height - often with a contorted trunk and branches as a response to extremes of wind, temperature and low nutrient supply. In less severe habitats - bog margins, lakeshores and protected coastlines - it can attain heights of 6 m, with an irregular ball-shaped crown of foliage restricted to the top third of the tree. The bark is greyish-black and furrowed into large shedding plates. The stiff needles, up to 7 cm long, are in bundles of 2. Male cones, in conspicuous clusters near the ends of branches, produce prodigious amounts of yellow pollen in summer. The immature red female cones on the tips of branches develop into a woody, cylindrical cone 2.5 - 5 cm long after pollination. The numerous, overlapping cone scales are oblong, with a thick, bluntly pointed apex. The seeds are not mature until 1 to 2 years following pollination.

Lodgepole Pine is common throughout the Islands, but is most abundant in both its dwarf and large form in the lowland bogs of north-east Graham Island. The tree is rarely found in the lowland Western Hemlock/Red Cedar forest. The species is widely distributed in western North America.

Key characteristics: Range in size from twisted bonsai to tree-size; long needles in groups of 2; cones cylindrical and scales with thickened woody tips.

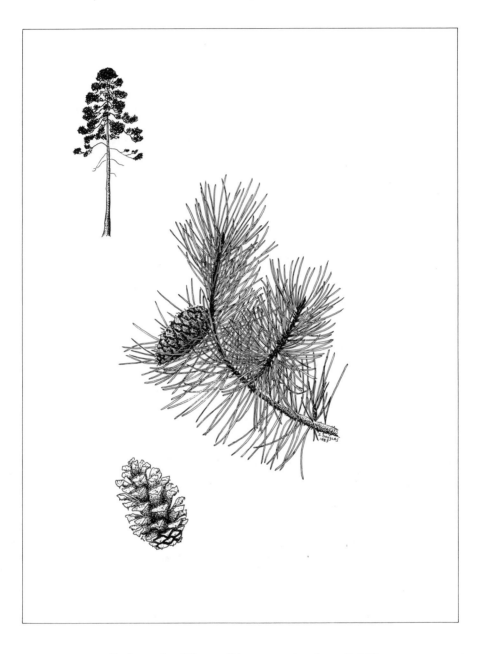

Lodgepole Pine, *Pinus contorta*. (X 3/5)

PINACEAE   PINE FAMILY

Tsuga heterophylla (Raf.) Sarg.   **Western Hemlock**

Western Hemlock has a narrow silhouette of horizontal or
drooping branches with dense pendant branchlets. It has a
horizontal or drooping leader (the growing apex of the
tree). On the Islands, Hemlock reaches a height of 50 m.
The bark is scaly to deeply furrowed and reddish-brown in
colour. The needle-like leaves are flat in cross-section
with a rounded tip; they are variable in length within a
branchlet, from 8 to 20 mm long and are all on the same
plane, forming horizontal sprays. The lower surface of the
needles are white. The oval cones, 1.5 to 2.5 cm long,
have only 4 or 5 ranks of broad wavy-margined scales and
extend from the tips of branchlets. Seeds mature in 1
season and are released from between the extended scales.

The lowland forests on the Islands are predominantly
Western Hemlock and Western Red Cedar; seedlings are shade
tolerant enough to grow beneath a full canopy. Western
Hemlock is found throughout the Islands, and in North
America, from California to Alaska.

The inner growing layer of the tree, the cambium, was a
food for most of the first nations people on the coast. It
was scraped from inside the bark and eaten fresh or dried
for later use. The Haida carved a variety of implements
and utensils from the strong wood.

Key characteristics: Drooping to horizontal leader; blunt
needles of unequal lengths, all in one plane with under-
surfaces white; cones oval, scales wavy-margined, broad.

Western Hemlock , *Tsuga heterophylla.* (X 3/5)

Tsuga mertensiana (Bong.) Carr.   **Mountain Hemlock**

Mountain Hemlock is a small tree on the Islands, reaching
a maximum of 7 m in height. It is often scrubby, with
densely clustered needles and branchlets. The bark is
dark-brown and furrowed. The plump 20 mm long needles are
green on both upper and lower surfaces. They are crowded
on the branches and project in all directions from the
stem. The 3 to 6 cm oblong cones are pendant on the tips
of branches. They have 8 to 10 ranks of overlapping scales
with slightly toothed margins which reflex back when the
cones are fully open. Mature seeds are released in the
winter after pollination.

On the Islands, Mountain Hemlock is widely distributed but
uncommon, except in subalpine habitats where it can form
continuous stands. In exposed areas, it is often a prostrate shrub. Its world distribution is western North
America from California to Alaska.

Key characteristics: Scrubby tree with densely crowded
needles; needles green on both surfaces; cones oblong;
scales reflexed back when seeds shed.

Mountain Hemlock, *Tsuga mertensiana*. (X 3/5)

Taxus brevifolia Nutt.   **Western Yew**

Yew is a small tree of 6 to 15 m on the Islands. It has few horizontal branches with drooping branchlets. The bark is scaly and reddish-purple and the wood itself is red, very hard and heavy. The needle-like leaves are 15 to 20 mm long, with a dark-green upper surface and a light green undersurface; the tips of the needles taper to a sharp point. The leaves are attached spirally on the stems but are twisted at the base so that sprays are flat and linear. The female cone, borne laterally on branchlets, consists of a single seed in a red berry-like covering. Male and female cones grow on different trees. The seeds mature in September and are eaten and dispersed by birds.

Yew is uncommon on the Islands, distributed sporadically in most forest habitats, lakeshores and bog margins. In North America, it grows along the west coast from California to southern Alaska.

Valued for its strength and hardness, Yew wood was used by the Haida, as well as most other coastal Indians, for eating and cooking implements and for wedges for splitting Red Cedar planks.

The bark of Yew contains a substance called taxol which has been recently found to be effective in suppressing tumours in breast and ovarian cancers.

Key characteristics: Scrubby tree with horizontal branches; needle-like leaves flat, pointed, pale green beneath; cone a red fleshy "berry" surrounding a single seed.

Western Yew, *Taxus brevifolia.* (X 3/5)

FLOWERING PLANTS

ARALIACEAE   GINSENG FAMILY

Oplopanax horridus (Smith) Miq.   **Devil's-Club**

Devil's-Club is a gangly, few-leaved shrub that grows up
to 3 m tall. The stalks, branches and leaf veins are armed
with stiff, sharp spines. The serrated leaves, up to 35
cm wide, have 5 to 7 lobes and spread horizontally on long
leaf stalks. Flowers are greenish-white, crowded into 15
cm long terminal clusters. The fruit is an oblong, slightly flattened red berry about 8 mm long.

Devil's-Club is rare on the Islands, growing primarily in
river valley forests, but occurring sporadically on the
coast. The plant was probably more common prior to the
introduction of Blacktail deer, which crop young plants.

The spines cause allergic responses in many people.
Although the stalk and root are used medicinally, the
berries are considered inedible by all coastal people.

Key characteristics: Gangly stalks armed with large, sharp
spines; broad lax leaves with spines on the leaf veins; a
cluster of small greenish-white flowers or red berries.

Devil's Club, *Oplopanax horridus*. (X 1/4)

35

BETULACEAE   BIRCH FAMILY

Alnus rubra Bong.   **Red Alder**

On the Islands, Red Alder is commonly a small tree, rarely
exceeding a height of 10 m. The leaves are deciduous,
coarsely toothed and have margins rolled tightly under.
They have a dull green undersurface and are rarely over 12
cm long. Bark is smooth and greenish-grey to blotchy white
and grey in colour. Both male and female catkins grow on
the same tree, with the conspicuous, long staminate (male)
catkins pendant, 4 or 5 to a cluster. Short pistillate
(female) catkins, in clusters of 4 to 6, are erect on
branchlets at the base of the staminate catkins. After
fertilization, the pistillate catkin develops into a
woody, oval cone that opens in the fall, releasing the
seeds.

Red Alder grows on the border of rivers, lakeshores and
beaches throughout the Islands. The largest trees, up to
20 m high, grow in the river valleys. It becomes abundant
as a small tree in disturbed and logged areas, sometimes
forming pure stands.

Catkins mature in March and seeds are released in the
fall. Alder is an important successional stage after log-
ging because it "fixes nitrogen". Bacteria live symbio-
tically in the rootlets of alder; they extract nitrogen
from the air and bind it to other elements, constructing
compounds that are usable by plants. The relatively rapid
decomposition of the leaves and plant body adds humus to
the soil for regeneration of the coniferous forest.

The Haida and other coastal groups used the bark as a red
or brown dye; the soft, bright-coloured wood was carved
into masks or implements such as dishes and spoons. At
present, as it was in the past, Red Alder is a preferred
wood for smoking fish.

Red Alder can be easily distinguished from its close
relative, **Sitka Alder** (*Alnus viridis* ssp. *sinuata*) (not
illustrated) which has an irregularly and sharply serrate
leaf margin that is not rolled under and a leaf under-

Red Alder, *Alnus rubra*. (X 1/2)

surface that is slightly shiny. In other characteristics, the 2 are almost indistinguishable. **Sitka Alder** is more common in mountain habitats and blanket bogs on Moresby Island and the west coast of Graham Island. It also reaches the coast in these areas, thriving at the head of coastal rock bluffs or gravel beaches.

Key characteristics: Deciduous tree producing catkins; leaves oval and coarsely toothed.

CAPRIFOLIACEAE   HONEYSUCKLE FAMILY

Lonicera involucrata (Rich.)   **Twinberry Honeysuckle**
Banks ex Sprengel

Twinberry Honeysuckle is a robust, deciduous shrub that grows up to 5 m tall. The leaves are elliptical, pointed and up to 13 cm long; they have a shiny green undersurface and are dull green above. They are distinctly angled upward and their clasping leaf stalks are opposite and paired on the branches. The muted yellow flowers are tubular in shape, 1 cm long, and always paired. Each of the flowers is subtended by a pair of small purple bracts and the inflorescence is pendant to horizontal on a long (up to 6 cm) flower stalk. The paired, shiny black berries are 10 mm in diameter.

Twinberry is scattered throughout the Islands close to the coast. It is rare inland, usually along lakeshores, and is absent from bog habitats.

Both hummingbirds and native bumblebees pollinate the flowers which develop in May and June; the berries are ripe by July. The edibility of Twinberry is a mystery - it is unknown what mammals or birds eat and disperse the berries. None of the First Nations people ate the fruits, considering them inedible, and they have a wide reputation as being poisonous to humans.

Key characteristics: Robust, deciduous shrub; paired yellow tubular flowers and paired black berries.

Twinberry Honeysuckle, *Lonicera involucrata.* (X 1/2)

CAPRIFOLIACEAE   HONEYSUCKLE FAMILY

Sambucus racemosa L. ssp. *pubens*   **Coastal Red Elder**
(Michx.) House

A many-branched shrub or small tree, Red Elder grows to
about 3 m in height. There are 5 to 7 lax, finely-toothed
leaflets in each compound leaf. A typical leaflet is about
8 cm long, but there is much variability in size. Leaflets
have a crumpled texture. Hundreds of white flowers, each
5 mm across with 5 reflexed petals, are clustered in a
pyramid-shaped inflorescence. The fruits are small (5 mm),
shiny red berries in terminal clusters.

Red Elder grows in open, sunny areas along rivers and on
the coast throughout the Islands. It is most abundant in
disturbed habitats along roads or at the edge of logged
areas.

The foamy inflorescences develop in May and berries are
ripe in July and August. The fruits were eaten in all
coastal Indian nations, usually cooked and preserved for
later use, but today the fruits are rarely used.

There are 3 kinds of trees in the Rose (Rosaceae) family
that can be mistaken for Red Elder, but none of them are
common. **European Mountain-Ash** (*Sorbus aucuparia*) (not
illustrated), a small tree native to Europe, is an escapee
from gardens on the Islands and can be found growing near
towns. It has 11 to 15 leaflets which are covered on their
lower surface with fine white hairs. **Sitka Mountain-Ash**
(*Sorbus sitchensis* ssp. *sitchensis* and *S. sitchensis* ssp.
grayi) (not illustrated) is native to the Islands, but is
rare, with subspecies *sitchensis* found along the coast or
rivers and *grayi* in the subalpine. Leaflets are 7 to 11
in number with an undersurface devoid of hairs or with
hairs only along the midvein; the tips of the leaflets are
rounded. Fruits are red or purplish.

Key characteristics: A small tree with compound leaves of
5 to 7 leaflets; white flowers or red berries in clusters
at the tips of branchlets.

40

Coastal Red Elder, *Sambucus racemosa* ssp. *pubens*. (X 1/4)

CAPRIFOLIACEAE   HONEYSUCKLE FAMILY

Symphoricarpos albus (L.) Blake   **Common Snowberry**

A deciduous shrub up to 2 m high, Snowberry has 2 - 5 cm
long, oval leaves oppositely attached to branches; they
may be shallowly lobed. Flowers are pink and open bell-
shaped, clustered at the ends of branchlets. The berry is
dull white, fleshy but dry, and about 15 mm in diameter.

Snowberry is never common, but has a scattered distribution on coastal Moresby Island and southern Graham
Island on rock bluffs and upper beach margins.

Snowberry flowers in July and the berries are developed in
late August, persisting into November. The fruits were not
eaten historically by the coastal people, who believed
them to be poisonous. As with Twinberry Honeysuckle, it's
not known what animals or birds disperse the berries, and
how serious an effect the berries have on humans.

Key characteristics: A deciduous shrub with terminal pink
flowers and tight clusters of dull white berries.

Viburnum edule (Michx.) Raf.   **High Bush Cranberry**

                                             Not illustrated

High Bush Cranberry is a 2 m high shrub. The leaves (5 to
8 cm long) are irregularly toothed, usually 3-lobed with
3 or 5 main veins diverging from the base of the leaf.
Small white flowers are clustered into inflorescences that
develop in the leaf axils. Small (less than 1 cm diameter)
shiny berries are red to orange, tart-tasting and contain
a flat seed.

This is a rare plant on the Islands, growing on lakeshores
and creeks on northern Moresby and central Graham Island.

Key characteristics: Toothed, lobed leaves; small white
flowers and red berries on pedicels in leaf axils.

Common Snowberry, *Symphoricarpos albus*. (X 1/2)

CORNACEAE   DOGWOOD FAMILY

Cornus sericea L. ssp.   **Western Red-osier Dogwood**
occidentalis (Torr. & Gray)
Fosberg   Not illustrated

Red twigs give the common name to Red-osier Dogwood, a
deciduous shrub reaching a maximum height of 6 m on the
Islands. The 8 cm long leaves, attached opposite on
branches, have smooth margins. Flowers have 4 white petals
only 4 mm long, and grow in loose clusters at the ends of
branches. The fruit is a white, round berry, containing a
single stone.

Red-osier Dogwood is rare on the Islands, occurring
sporadically in river valleys and on the coast on southern
Graham and northern Moresby Island.

Key characteristics: Red twigs and branchlets; minute
white flowers or white berries in loose clusters.

EMPETRACEAE   CROWBERRY FAMILY

Empetrum nigrum L.   **Black Crowberry**

An evergreen branched shrub up to 20 cm tall, Crowberry
often forms a dense ground cover. The thick leaves, 5 mm
long and triangular in cross section, are in close whorls
up the stalk and branches. The red flowers are small
(about 5 mm across) and inconspicuous, growing close to
the stem near the branch apex. Male and female flowers are
usually on different plants, but occasionally plants have
both sexes on the same plant or within a single flower.
The flowers have 3 petals; male flowers have 3 long
stamens and female flowers have a short style. Crowberry
fruit is a black acidic berry up to 1 cm in diameter.

Crowberry is common in bogs and subalpine habitats
throughout the Islands; it grows all across Canada and
northern Eurasia in suitable habitats.

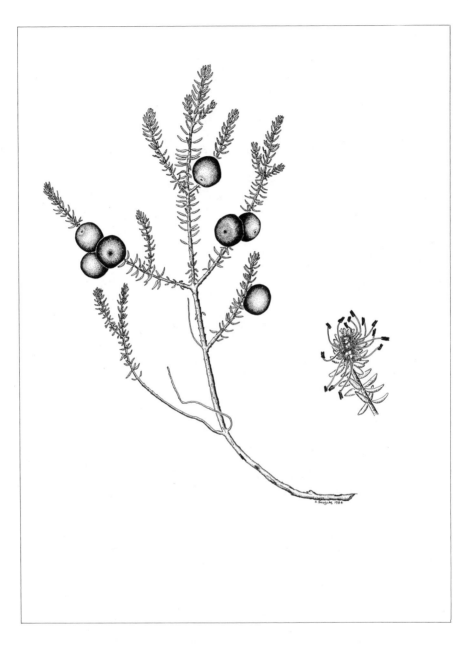

Black Crowberry, *Empetrum nigrum*. (Branch x 1; flower x 2)

Black Crowberry is the first plant to flower on the bog in April to early May. The juicy but acidic berries were not eaten historically by the Haida people. But this abundance of fruit is harvested, and the seeds dispersed, by birds such as Dark-eyed Junco, Blue Grouse and Canada Geese and by Deer Mice. The berries are ripe from June to September.

Key characteristics: Small upright bog shrub; numerous tiny leaves; berries dull black.

ERICACEAE   HEATH FAMILY

Andromeda polifolia L.   **Bog Rosemary**

Bog Rosemary is an upright, few-branched shrub 10 - 25 cm high. The 20 mm long leaves are linear with inrolled margins angled upwards on the plant; the upper surface is dull with prominent transverse veins. Flowers are about 8 mm long, pink in colour and urn-shaped with 5 reflexed corolla tips. Seeds are contained in a 5-lobed capsule.

The plant is abundant in bogs where it grows primarily on hummocks of *Sphagnum* moss. It is found throughout the Islands wherever bog habitat is available.

Plants on the Islands flower mid-may to June, and then have a sporadic second flowering from mid-August into the fall. They are pollinated by native bumblebees.

Key characteristics: Diminutive shrub with few dull green, upward angled leaves; pink, urn-shaped flowers.

Loiseleuria procumbens (L.) Desv.   **Alpine-azalea**

Alpine-azalea is a prostrate, evergreen shrub with inter-twining woody branches reaching 10 cm off the ground. The tightly clustered oblong leaves (about 5 mm long) have inrolled margins, a waxy upper surface and dull under-surface. The small pink flowers (about 5 mm across) are

Bog Rosemary, *Andromeda polifolia*. (X 1)
Alpine-azalea, *Loiseleuria procumbens*. (X 1)

47

clustered at the tips of branches; they are broadly bell-shaped with 5 corolla lobes and 5 stamens. The fruit is an oval seed capsule about 4 mm long.

The name Alpine-azalea is apt for the shrub over much of its world distribution in mountainous areas of the north-west Pacific and Scandinavia, but on the Islands it is common in lowland bogs as well as in subalpine areas.

Alpine-azalea flowers, appearing in mid-May on the Islands, are small enough to be overlooked, but the robust woody stems are characteristic, as is its habitat along the margins of bog pools.

Key characteristics: A low, tangled growth habit; small pink open bell-shaped flowers.

ERICACEAE   HEATH FAMILY

Cassiope lycopodioides (Pall.) D. Don   **Club-moss Cassiope**
ssp. *cristapilosa* Calder & Taylor

Club-moss Cassiope is a low trailing shrub, with branches prostrate or arching. The 2 to 3 mm long fleshy leaves overlap each other and are tightly pressed against the stem in four longitudinal rows. The bell-shaped white flowers, 7 mm long, have reflexed corolla tips and are pendant on long stalks, solitary or grouped near the ends of branches. The fruit is a small round capsule. Sub-species *cristapilosa* is endemic to the Queen Charlotte Islands and has as its most distinct characteristic minute curled hairs on each leaf tip.

This species of Cassiope is common in subalpine and alpine habitats, including rock outcrops in blanket bogs. It reaches sea level in dry, rocky habitats.

Merten's Cassiope (*Cassiope mertensiana*) (not illustrated) can be distinguished from Club-moss Cassiope by a larger stem diameter and flower size; it does not have hairs on the leaf tips. Merten's Cassiope is rare on the Islands,

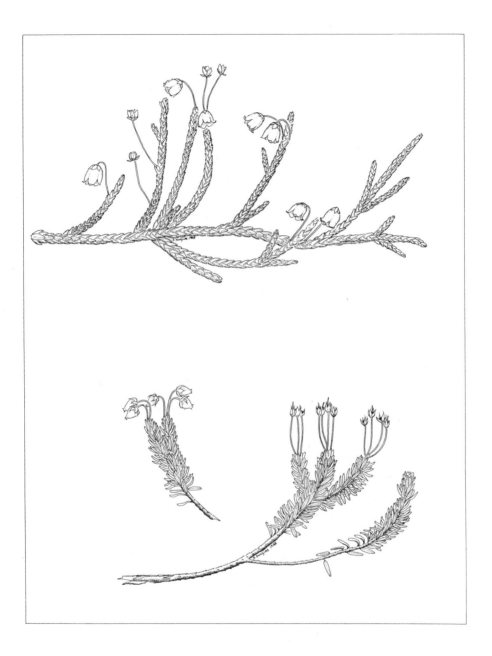

Club-moss Cassiope, *Cassiope lycopodioides* ssp.
cristapilosa. (X 3/4)
Cream Mountain-heather, *Phyllodoce glanduliflora*.
(X 1/2)

49

found only in alpine habitat in the mountain ranges in southwest Graham Island and western Moresby Island.

Key characteristics: Tightly overlapping leaves; leaf tips with curled hairs; white, bell-shaped flowers.

ERICACEAE   HEATH FAMILY

Cassiope stelleriana (Pallas) DC   **Steller's Cassiope**

Not illustrated

An evergreen, sprawling shrub up to 10 cm tall, Steller's Cassiope has leaves that are 5 mm long and spreading, rather than tightly pressed against the stem as in Club-moss Cassiope. The open bell-shaped flowers are white or pinkish, 6 mm long, and solitary on short pedicels at the tips of branches. The fruit is a small capsule.

Steller's Cassiope is abundant in the alpine areas on both Graham and Moresby Islands.

The plant is similar in appearance to Black Crowberry (*Empetrum nigrum*) in its vegetative state, but Crowberry has minute pink, flowers and black fleshy berries.

Key characteristics: Alpine heath with spreading leaves; white to pink flowers on short pedicels.

Phyllodoce glanduliflora (Hook.)   **Cream Mountain-heather**
Coville

Cream Mountain-heather (illustrated page 49) is a low, evergreen matted shrub up to 20 cm tall. The small (10 mm long), needle-like leaves have inrolled margins and are covered in fine hairs; they are attached alternately to

50

the stem. The flowers are yellow to green-tinged, about 8 mm long and urn-shaped with a very narrow opening at the tip. The corolla, sepals and flower stalks are covered with a dense coat of fine hairs. The seed capsule, about 4 mm long, is erect when mature.

The species is common in alpine habitats throughout the Islands and grows sporadically at lower elevations in exposed subalpine habitats.

Key characteristics: Alpine heath with needle-like leaves; yellow urn-shaped flowers.

ERICACEAE   HEATH FAMILY

Cladothamnus pyrolaeflorus Bong.   **Copperbush**

                                        Not illustrated

Copperbush is a deciduous spreading shrub up to 3 m tall. The 4 cm long leaves are thin and elliptical with blunt apices and no leaf stalks. The solitary flowers are up to 2 cm across, with 5 pink-copper coloured petals, 10 stamens and a long (1 cm) style that is hooked at the apex. The seed capsule is up to 7 mm wide.

Copperbush is scattered on the Islands and is never a conspicuous part of the vegetation. It grows on coastal rock shores, along lakeshores or river banks but is most common in clear areas in the subalpine.

Key characteristics: A spreading copper-tinged flower with a long hooked style.

ERICACEAE   HEATH FAMILY

Gaultheria shallon Pursh   **Salal**

Salal is a many-branched, evergreen shrub that can reach
heights of 2.5 m. The shiny green leaves are up to 12 cm
long. The white to pink urn-shaped flowers (up to 10 mm
long) have 5 reflexed tips and develop in long racemes of
up to 15 flowers. Often the flowers, flower stalks and
raceme branchlets are sticky. Salal fruits are purplish-
black, large (10 mm in diameter) and juicy, covered with
fine hairs.

Salal is ubiquitous at low elevations throughout the
Islands, occupying almost all habitats. The world dis-
tribution of the species is from British Columbia to
Southern California.

Salal has a long flowering season, from late June to
September. Flower color varies according to light exposure, from pure white in the shady forest to deep pink
in full sunlight. Salal berries ripen in August and
persist throughout the fall, a plentiful source of food
for birds and Black Bear.

As a food for humans, it is unmatched for its abundance
and was a staple food for all of the coastal Indians,
whether eaten fresh or dried for winter use. At present,
its whole-hearted use has waned, along with other
traditional foods, and its unusual taste dissuades many
new Islanders from eating it. The plant's ability to
thrive in many habitats - bog, shady forest, wind-swept
coastal rock - is a tribute to its hardiness.

Key characteristics: Erect, large-leaved shrub; white to
red flowers and purplish-black berries on long racemes.

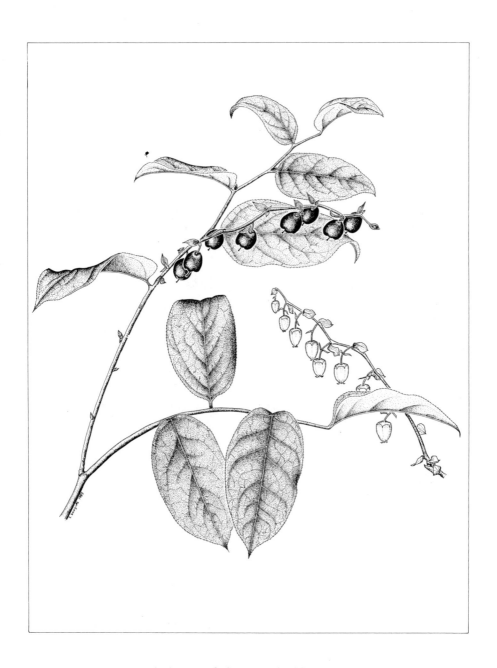

Salal, *Gaultheria shallon.* (X 1/2)

Kalmia microphylla (Hook.) Heller   **Western Swamp Kalmia**
ssp. *occidentalis* (Small) Taylor and   **Swamp Laurel**
MacBryde

Swamp laurel is a few-leaved, 30 - 50 cm tall shrub that is upright and evergreen. The narrow 4 cm long leaves have a shiny upper surface with a white mid-vein, a dull whitish under-surface and inrolled leaf margins. The leaves angle upwards and grow near the apex of the stem. The rose-pink, saucer-shaped flowers (about 2 cm across) consist of 5 fused, lobed petals. Ten stamens radiate from the centre, each with its anther in a "pocket" formed by folds in the corolla. The fruit is a 5-segmented seed capsule, about 5 mm long.

In raised and blanket bogs, Swamp Laurel is common throughout the Islands and all across northern Canada.

Swamp Laurel flowers in June on the Islands, attracting native bumblebees as pollinators. An active toxin in the leaves makes the plant noxious to grazers; it may be poisonous to humans.

Non-flowering Laurel may be confused with Labrador Tea (*Ledum groenlandicum*) which, although it has a similar leaf shape, has a woolly undersurface. Bog Rosemary (*Andromeda polifolia*) has a similar leaf shape, but is less than half the size of Swamp Laurel.

Key characteristics: Leaves with shiny upper surface; circular rose-pink flowers with 10 stamens.

Western Swamp Kalmia, *Kalmia microphylla* ssp.
occidentalis. (X 3/4)

ERICACEAE   HEATH FAMILY

Ledum groenlandicum Oeder   **Common Labrador Tea**

Labrador Tea is a gangly shrub growing up to 1 m tall. The
4.5 cm long leaves, arranged alternately near the apex of
the woody stem, are elliptical and leathery with inrolled
edges. The upper surface of the leaf is dull and the
under-surface is woolly, with sparse white hairs on young
leaves becoming rust-coloured and dense as the leaves
mature. The 12 mm wide flowers have 5 or 6 white petals
and 5 to 10 stamens and are clustered on long pedicels at
the apex of the plant. The fruit is a small capsule that
is retained on the plant after the seeds are released and
throughout the next year's flowering season.

Labrador Tea is widely distributed in bogs and other
poorly-drained areas on the Islands. It grows throughout
northern and coastal Canada.

On the Islands, Labrador Tea flowers in June and early
July. This is probably the most familiar of the bog plants
because its leathery leaves have been used historically to
make tea in North America. It is possible that the Haida
originally used the leaves only medicinally, for sore
throats and colds; the Haida word for it as a tea is of
recent origin.

Labrador Tea should not be confused with the toxic Swamp
Laurel (*Kalmia microphylla* ssp. *occidentalis*) which has
shiny, naked leaves and pink flowers.

Key characteristics: Sparse-leaved bog shrub; linear
leaves with a woolly under-surface; terminal cluster of
white spreading flowers.

Common **Labrador Tea**, *Ledum groenlandicum*. (X 1/2)

Menziesia ferruginea Smith   **Rusty Pacific Menziesia**

Pacific Menziesia is a deciduous shrub up to 3 m tall. The thin, lax leaves are elliptical (about 6 cm long), pale green and finely hairy on the upper surface; they are usually in groups of 5. The flowers are clustered at the base of the year's new growth and are pendant on long flower stalks. The greenish-pink to copper corollas, up to 10 mm long, are urn-shaped with 4 reflexed corolla tips. After pollination, the corollas fall and the flower pedicels become erect again, holding the 7 mm long seed capsules vertical. Each year's new growth - twigs, leaves and flower stalks - is covered in fine hairs.

Pacific Menziesia is a common shrub in the forest under-story that grows throughout the Islands wherever mixed shade conditions are found. Flowers develop in June and the seeds set by August.

Key characteristics: A rangy shrub with elliptical thin finely hairy leaves clustered in groups of 5; coppery urn-shaped flowers.

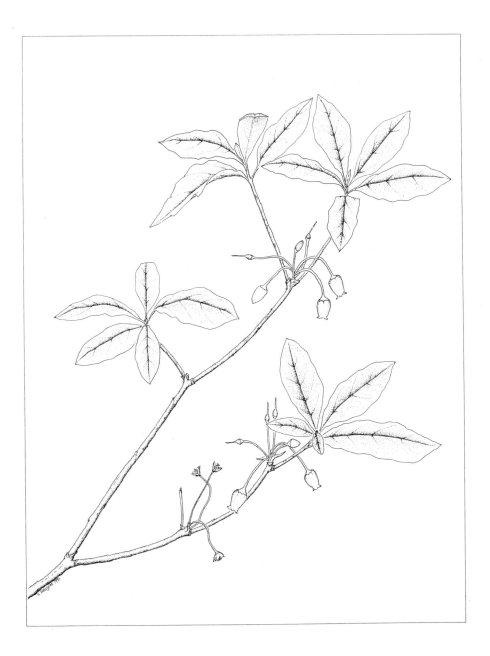

Rusty Pacific Menziesia, *Menziesia ferruginea*. (X 1/2)

Vaccinium alaskaense Howell   **Alaskan Blueberry**
                                                 Blue Huckleberry

Alaskan Blueberry is a shrub 2 - 3 m tall; branches are
characteristically round in cross section. The leaves are
oval and thin, with a maximum length of 6 cm, but are much
smaller in areas exposed to full sunlight. The 8 mm long
flowers are bronze-pink in colour, urn-shaped but squat,
with the 5 corolla tips rarely reflexed back. The flower
stalk is swollen at its attachment to the flower and the
style usually projects beyond the corolla mouth slightly.
The flowers open when leaves are partly developed. The
fruit is a tart, purplish-black berry up to 12 mm in
diameter.

Throughout the Islands, Alaskan Blueberry is sparsely
distributed as a forest understorey shrub and in this
habitat is tall and gangly, with few large leaves and few
berries. On forest margins, lakeshores, river banks and as
an early succession shrub in logged forests, the plant is
abundant, forming dense stands.

Flowers open in late March and early April, and berries
are ripe by early July. Alaskan Blueberry and Oval-leaved
Blueberry (*Vaccinium ovalifolium*) are known locally as
Blue Huckleberry and the two species are rarely distinguished. The berries of both species are used by Islanders
for pies and jams, and are canned or frozen for year-round
use. Traditionally, the Haida and all coastal Indian
groups ate Blue Huckleberries, both fresh or dried in
cakes. They distinguished the 2 species by their different
fruiting times and slightly different taste, Oval-leaved
Blueberry being sweeter. The berries are food for many
bird species and especially for Black Bear; the distribution of shrubs along rivers and in river valleys may be
the result of bears eating the berries and defecating the
seeds while ranging through their territories.

Alaskan Blueberry and Oval-leaved Blueberry are difficult
to distinguish when in fruit, but Oval-leaved Blueberry
has a sweeter taste and a whitish bloom to the berry. In

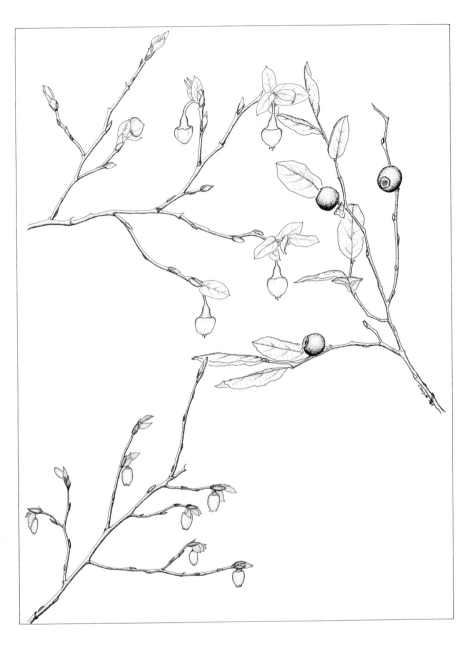

Alaskan Blueberry, *Vaccinium alaskaense*. (X 3/4)
Oval-leaved Blueberry, *V. ovalifolium*. (X 3/4)

general, Alaskan Blueberry is a more robust plant with larger leaves, but there is considerable overlap in size in different habitats. While in flower, the 2 species can be easily distinguished: Oval-leaved has smaller pinkish flowers with reflexed tips, a style not exerted beyond the corolla opening and no swollen portion to the flower stalk. Oval-leaved Blueberry flowers open before the leaves are developed. In both species, the stems and branches are round in cross section; this characteristic distinguishes them from Red Huckleberry (*Vaccinium parvifolium*) which has branches that are always angled, almost square, in cross section.

Key characteristics: Bronze-pink squat flowers that open as the leaves develop; pedicels swollen above corolla; berries blue-black, shiny.

ERICACEAE   HEATH FAMILY

Vaccinium ovalifolium Smith   Oval-leaved Blueberry
in Rees   Blue Huckleberry

Oval-leaved Blueberry (illustrated on p. 61) is a shrub of less than 2 m tall; branches are round in cross section. The leaves are oval to elliptical, thin and up to 4 cm long, although there is considerable variation in leaf size (and bushiness of the shrub) depending on the light available; in sunny habitats leaves are smaller. Flowers are white to deep pink in colour, urn-shaped and pendant with 5 reflexed tips; the style does not project beyond the mouth of the 7 mm long corolla. Flowers always bloom before the leaves develop. The fruit is a sweet-tasting, blue berry, maximum 10 mm across, with a whitish bloom.

The distribution of Oval-leaved Blueberry overlaps that of Alaskan Blueberry; it is sparsely distributed as an understorey shrub throughout the Islands' forests and is more abundant along water courses and in logged areas.

Oval-leaved Blueberry is the first of the Islands' shrubs to flower, as early as the middle of March. Berries appear

in late June and July. The berries are, and were traditionally, used as a food (see Alaskan Blueberry).

Oval-leaved Blueberry is difficult to distinguish from
Alaskan Blueberry vegetatively or in fruit; their
differences are discussed under Alaskan Blueberry.

Key characteristics: Pink, urn-shaped flowers with
reflexed tips appearing before the leaves open; berries
blue with a white bloom.

ERICACEAE   HEATH FAMILY

Vaccinium caespitosum Michx.   **Dwarf Blueberry**

                                            Not illustrated

Dwarf Blueberry is a low, spreading shrub with upright
branches rarely over 15 cm tall. The leaves, 25 mm long,
are thin, bright green and finely toothed on the apical
half. The 6 mm long pink to pink-red flowers are narrowly
urn-shaped, pendant, with 5 reflexed corolla tips. The
edible berries are blackish-blue with a pale bloom,
usually 6 mm in diameter.

Dwarf Blueberry is never common and rarely produces fruit,
but can be found in bogs and in the subalpine throughout
the Islands. Bog Blueberry (*Vaccinium uliginosum*) can be
distinguished from Dwarf Blueberry by its blue-green
leaves with smooth margins.

Key characteristics: Low bog shrub; thin, bright green,
serrated leaves; pink flowers narrowly urn-shaped;
blue-black berries.

ERICACEAE   HEATH FAMILY

Vaccinium oxycoccus L.   **Bog Cranberry**

Bog cranberry is a diminutive evergreen shrub with thin
trailing branches. The 7 mm long, elliptical leaves are
shiny on the upper surface and pale beneath, widely spaced
along the prostrate branches. The deep pink flowers are 10
mm long with 8 stamens forming a 'beak' in front of the 4
strongly reflexed petals; long, thread-like pedicels hold
the flowers off the ground. The fruit is an oval cranberry
up to 12 mm in diameter, pale green when immature, ripening to a red-purple. The berry is firm and acidic, soft-
ening and sweetening only slightly after a frost. When in
fruit, the berries lie on the moss-covered ground, the
thin pedicels unable to support them.

Bog cranberry is abundant in the wettest parts of the bog
and in swamps throughout the Islands.

The flowers open in June and although the berries begin
developing in August, they do not ripen until October.
Some fruits persist on the plants until the following
spring, and are an important food for overwintering birds.
Bog cranberries were collected by the Haida in the fall
and stored in boxes until they ripened. At present they
are the favoured fruit for Christmas cranberry sauce.

Key characteristics: Tiny prostrate shrub; flowers with
pink reflexed petals; berries oval, red-purple, ripening
in late fall.

Bog Cranberry, *Vaccinium oxycoccus*. (X 1)

ERICACEAE   HEATH FAMILY

Vaccinium parvifolium Smith in Rees   **Red Huckleberry**

Red Huckleberry is a shrub up to 3 m tall in shady forest conditions, but is generally smaller and more bushy in exposed habitats. The branches and stems are always angled, such that they appear square in cross section. The deciduous leaves are oval (maximum 3 cm long), thin, with a smooth margin; very young plants (less than about 20 cm high) have serrated leaf margins. The flowers are small (5 mm long), urn-shaped, and squat, with 5 reflexed corolla tips; the greenish-pink flowers develop after the leaves are fully opened. The fruit is a bright red to pink berry up to 10 mm across, but there is great variation in shape, size and taste among plants.

Red Huckleberry is a common shrub in the forest understory, where it produces few leaves or berries. On lakeshores, forest edges and as an early succession plant after forests are logged, it is more abundant and produces copious fruit. It is found throughout the Islands, except in alpine areas.

Flowering begins in April and berries are ripe by late July. Red Huckleberry is a treasured fruit on the Islands, traditionally by the Haida, who ate the berries fresh or stored them whole for winter use, and today, when berries are eaten fresh, are canned or frozen and made into pies, syrups and jams.

Red Huckleberry can be distinguished from the closely related Alaskan and Oval-leaved Blueberries by its angled branches, later flowering and red berries.

Key characteristics: Branches angled in cross section; small, greenish-pink urn-shaped flowers that open after the leaves are developed; round, red berries.

Red Huckleberry, *Vaccinium parvifolium*. (X 1)

Vaccinium uliginosum L. ssp.   **Bog Blueberry**
occidentale (Gray) Hulten

Bog blueberry is a low (30 cm) many-branched deciduous
shrub. The 15 mm long, oval leaves are flat, smooth mar-
gined and have a bluish cast. Flowers are pink, urn-
shaped, with 4 or 5 reflexed corolla tips and 8 to 10
stamens. The 6 mm long flowers are pendant and partially
hidden by the leaves. The fruit is a firm, blue berry with
a whitish bloom and white flesh, about 8 mm in diameter.

The shrub is a common plant on bogs throughout the Islands
and in subalpine habitats; the species is found in similar
habitats throughout northern Canada, Europe and Asia.

Bog Blueberry flowers from June to mid-July. Berries,
which are ripe from August to mid-September, are edible
but bland. The dark berries are not easily visible,
half-hidden beneath the bluish leaves; this may account
for their apparent rarity. Resident birds such as
Dark-eyed Junco, Sandhill Crane and Blue Grouse feed on
the berries.

Key characteristics: Low bog shrub; thin, slightly blue
leaves with smooth margins; pink urn-shaped flowers; blue
berries with white flesh.

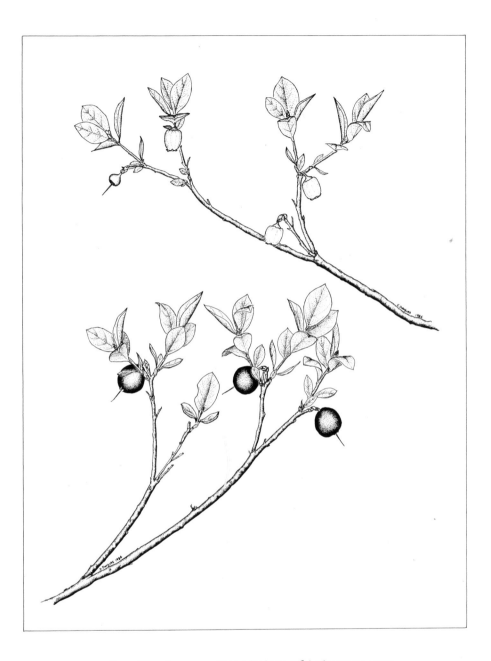

Bog Blueberry, *Vaccinium uliginosum* ssp.
occidentale. (X 3/4)

Vaccinium vitis-idaea L. ssp.   **Mountain Cranberry**
minus (Lodd.) Hulten

An evergreen few-branched shrub, Mountain Cranberry is rarely over 15 cm tall. The 10 - 15 mm, oval leaves have inrolled margins, and are shiny green on the upper surface and dull green beneath. The 4-lobed, bell-shaped flowers, 6 mm long, are pendant and clustered at the ends of branches; they vary in colour from white to pink. The fruit is a shiny red, oblong berry about 10 mm long that has firm, acidic flesh.

Mountain cranberry grows along the fringes of the bog, usually in drier raised areas, along lakeshores and forest margins and in the subalpine. It grows all across northern areas of the globe.

The flowers develop in June and berries are ripe from mid-September until early November. Traditionally, the Haida collected the berries and stored them for winter use. Although the berries are widely used as a preserve in Scandinavian countries, on the Islands, they are rarely eaten today.

Key characteristics: Shiny green leaves with inrolled margins, white to pink bell-shaped flowers; fruit a small berry.

Arctostaphylos uva-ursi (L.) Sprengel   **Kinnikinnick**

Not illustrated

Kinnikinnick is a low, trailing, evergreen shrub with thick, oblong leaves up to 2.5 cm long. The flowers are pinkish-white to deep red, narrowly urn-shaped and about 5 mm long. The 8 mm fruit is a red berry with white flesh, resembling a small apple in shape.

Kinnikinnick is uncommon on the Islands, growing only on

70

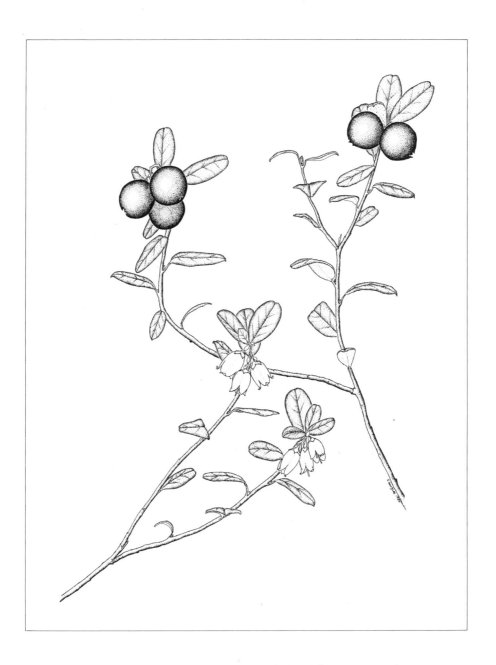

Mountain Cranberry, *Vaccinium vitis-idaea* ssp. *minus*. (X 1)

rocky coastal headlands and exposed beaches in Skidegate Inlet and the east coast of Moresby Island.

Flowers appear in May and June and the berries are ripe in July. The berries were eaten by the Haida and other coastal Indians, but the real value of the plant was in its leaves, which were smoked like tobacco.

Key characteristics: A trailing shrub; oblong leaves without inrolled margins; pinkish-white urn-shaped flowers; red berries.

FABACEAE   PEA FAMILY

Cytisus scoparius (L.) Link   **Scotch Broom**

Scotch Broom, not native to the Islands, is a bushy shrub up to 2 m high. Branches and twigs are stiff, and angled in cross section. There is great variation in leaf shape. Leaves near the base of the branches are compound, about 2 cm long, with 3 elliptical leaflets, while those at the tips of branches are small and single. The 3 cm high flowers are typical 'pea flowers' with 5 petals - 1 upper, 2 lateral and 2 lower petals which enclose the reproductive parts. There are 2 colour forms, one with yellow flowers and one with yellow and purple flowers. The seeds ripen in a 5 cm long pod that is edged with fine hairs.

This European import is established on open, dry sites in disturbed habitats. There are large roadside colonies near Tlell, Graham Island. Scotch Broom flowers in June and July on the Islands and the pods develop in late July.

Common Gorse (*Ulex europaeus* L.), another European plant that is established along roadsides, is similar to Scotch Broom, but has leaves reduced to spines.

Key characteristics: Stiff-branched, thicket-forming shrub; small trifoliate or simple leaves; yellow or yellow and purple pea-like flowers; pods with hairy edges.

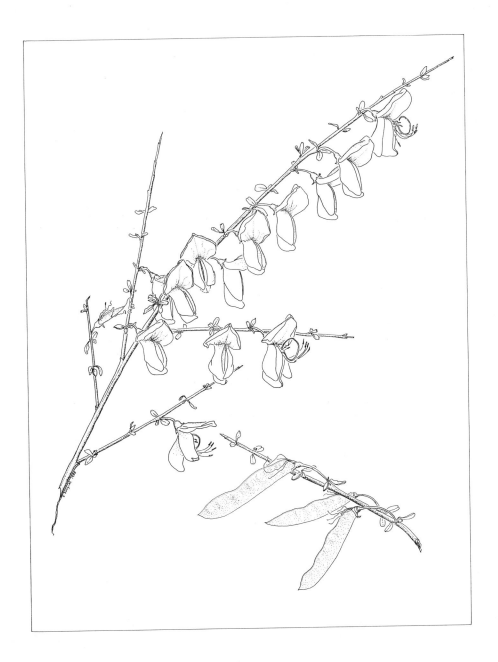

Scotch Broom, *Cytisus scoparius.* (X 1/2)

Ribes bracteosum Dougl. in Hook.   **Stink Currant**

Stink Currant is a rangy, deciduous shrub that rarely
exceeds 3 m in height. The branches are unspined and the
plant as a whole has a musky smell, similar to the cult-
ivated Black Currant. The leaves, up to 15 cm broad, are
5- to 7-lobed, coarsely toothed and have pale resin spots
on the under-surface. The white to greenish flowers grow
on a 20 cm long, erect flowering raceme. The fruit is a
dull bluish-grey berry with dark resin spots on the
surface.

Stink currant is uncommon, but has an Island-wide distribution, growing along river banks, beach margins or in
forest clearings.

As with Black Swamp Gooseberry (*Ribes lacustre*) and
Trailing Black Currant (*R. laxiflorum*), Stink Currant was
eaten by all of the coastal Indians, including the Haida,
according to the abundance of the plant, but none of the
species were considered as choice fruit.

Key characteristics: Nonspined, tall shrub with 5- to
7-lobed, maple-like leaves; white flowers and bluish-grey
berries on thin, erect stalks.

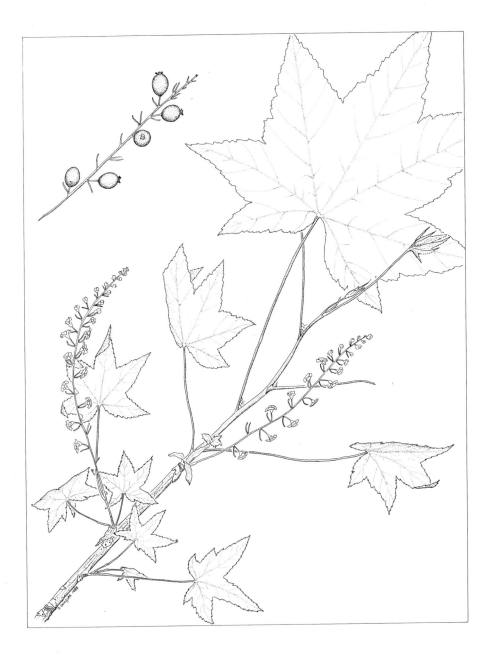

Stink Currant, *Ribes bracteosum.* (X 1/2)

75

Ribes lacustre (Pers.) Poir.   **Black Swamp Gooseberry**
in Lam.

Swamp Gooseberry is a deciduous shrub up to 1.5 m tall
armed with many small spines. The leaves are thin, 5-lobed
and serrate, about 5 cm across. The saucer-shaped flowers
are creamy white with pink margins, 6 mm across and faint-
ly sweet smelling. Multiple flowers are borne on pendant
(up to 7 cm long) racemes. The small fruits are dark
purple and covered in bristles.

Swamp Gooseberry grows on coastal rocky bluffs and river
banks on southern Graham Island and eastern Moresby
Island. It is scattered in natural habitats but becomes
abundant in disturbed areas. The edible fruits are difficult to pick because of the sharp spines, and were thus
ignored by many coastal Indian groups.

Key characteristics: A small, spiny shrub; 5-lobed,
serrate leaves; small flowers creamy to pink; purple,
bristly berries.

Ribes laxiflorum Pursh   **Trailing Black Currant**

                                        Not illustrated

Trailing Black Currant is a deciduous shrub usually less
than 1 m tall with unspined branches. The 5-lobed leaves
are coarsely toothed, up to 10 cm wide and have small red
glands on the lower leaf surface. The flowers are red and
white on erect flowering stalks. The fruit is a purplish-
black berry up to 1 cm in diameter, covered in fine hairs.

This species of Currant is scattered, but widely distributed on the Islands on rock bluffs, along forest margins
and in partially shaded clearings in the forest, typically
on the overturned roots of deadfall trees.

Similar to the other species in the Gooseberry Family,

Black Swamp Gooseberry, *Ribes lacustre*. (X 1/2)

Trailing Black Currant was not abundant enough to be an important winter food for the Haida, and was usually eaten fresh.

Key characteristics: A tall shrub with nonspined branches; 5-lobed leaves with reddish glands beneath; flowers red and white; berries purplish-black with fine hairs.

MYRICACEAE   BAYBERRY FAMILY

Myrica gale L.   **Sweet Gale**

Not illustrated

Sweet Gale is a deciduous spreading shrub of up to 1 m in height. The dull green, oblong leaves, about 4 cm long, have a few broad teeth near the apex and minute, shiny resin dots on both surfaces. When crushed, the leaves are aromatic. Inconspicuous brown catkins develop in the leaf axils in May, before the leaves develop; the fruit is a tiny nut.

On the Islands, Sweet Gale has a sporadic distribution in bogs, swampy areas and lakeshores. It is one of the few plants on the Islands that contains nitrogen-fixing bacteria in the root nodules (see Red Alder).

Key characteristics: Low deciduous shrub; leaves with resin dots, toothed at apex; inconspicuous catkins.

ROSACEAE   ROSE FAMILY

Amelanchier alnifolia Nutt. var.   **Pacific Saskatoon**
semiintegrifolia (Hook.) C.L. Hitchc.

Not illustrated

Pacific Saskatoon is a deciduous shrub or small tree reaching a height of 5 m on the Islands. The 3 cm long,

78

oval leaves are bluish tinged, with margins toothed along the apical half only; they are attached alternately to branches. The large (2.5 cm wide) white flowers are clustered on branchlets and have 5 petals. The fruit is a bluish-purple berry, 1 cm across, with sepals persistent at the apex of the fruit.

Pacific Saskatoon is uncommon on the Islands, growing on coastal rock bluffs and wind-exposed beaches on southeast Graham Island and the east coast of Moresby Island.

The flowers develop in May and fruit is set by August. Although Saskatoon berries were eaten traditionally by the Haida and are picked today as well, they are not abundant enough to be an important fruit on the Islands.

Key characteristics: Small, deciduous tree; bluish leaves toothed apically; clustered white flowers; bluish-purple berries.

ROSACEAE   ROSE FAMILY

Crataegus douglasii Lindl.   **Black Hawthorn**

                                               Not illustrated

A deciduous shrub or small tree, Black Hawthorn has branches armed with 1 to 2 cm long thorns. The leaves are thick, deep green and coarsely toothed, unlobed and up to 5 cm long. The 5-petalled white flowers are clustered at the ends of branchlets. The fruit is shiny black, with the sepals persistent at the apex of the 10 mm diameter berry.

Hawthorn is rare on the Islands, with several trees growing in Queen Charlotte City. Its usual habitat is along rivers, lakeshores and in dry coastal areas.

Key characteristics: Small tree armed with long thorns; leaves toothed; clustered white flowers or black fruit.

ROSACEAE   ROSE FAMILY

Malus fusca (Raf.) C.K. Schneid.   **Pacific Crab Apple**

On the Islands, Pacific Crab Apple is a small tree, rarely exceeding a height of 5 m. The deciduous leaves are roughly oval, coarsely toothed and usually have a pointed lobe on one edge of the leaf; they are arranged alternately on branches with a maximum length of 10 cm. Flowers are in clusters of up to a dozen on the ends of branchlets, white to pink in colour, with 5 petals and numerous anthers. Each flower is about 3 cm across. The fruits are small tart apples, yellow to red in colour and 10 to 15 mm long, that are clustered together on long pedicels. The previous years branchlets form hard, sharp thorns.

Crab Apple never forms pure stands on the Islands, but the trees can be locally common on sheltered beaches and lakeshores throughout the Islands.

Flowers develop in June over most of the Islands and the fruit is ripe by early September. The apples were extensively used by the Haida, who stored them in boxes for winter use. Presently, Islanders make crabapple jelly and occasionally use the hard wood as a fuel for smoking fish.

Key characteristics: A small tree with long 'thorns' formed from old branchlets; asymmetrical leaves; fruit a small tart apple.

Pacific Crab Apple, *Malus fusca.* (X 1/2)

ROSACEAE   ROSE FAMILY

Rosa nutkana Presl   **Nootka Rose**

Nootka Rose is a sprawling shrub up to 3 m high. The older
branches have large spines and the new growth, prickles;
branches are tinged with red. The compound leaf is made
up of 5 to 9 oval, finely toothed leaflets with the largest leaflets about 6 cm long. The showy, rose-pink flowers
have 5 spreading petals and numerous yellow stamens; they
are about 5 cm across and are borne singly on the ends of
branches. The rosehips, as the fruits are commonly called,
have an edible, red, fleshy rind, numerous seeds and
persistent sepals at the apex of the fruit.

Nootka Rose is scattered throughout coastal areas on the
Islands, at the heads of beaches and in cleared areas in
the forest near the coast.

Flowers develop in June and early July and the rosehips
are ripe by August. The fruit was eaten historically by
the Haida and, although rosehips are used in other parts
of world for jam, syrup and tea, it is not popular today
on the Islands as a food.

Key characteristics: Large shrub armed with spines; compound leaf of 5 to 9 leaflets; flower rose-pink; fruit a
rosehip.

Nootka Rose, *Rosa nutkana*. (X 1/2)

Rubus parviflorus Nutt.   **Western Thimbleberry**

Thimbleberry is a bushy shrub up to 2 m high. The lax,
light green leaves have fine hairs on the undersurface,
and are sparsely fuzzy above; they are finely toothed and
large (up to 25 cm across) with 5 to 7 pointed lobes.
Flowers are white, with 5 wrinkled petals and numerous
anthers, reaching a maximum width of 4.5 cm. The common
name describes the 2 cm wide fruit very well - a dull red
thimble-shaped compound berry that is dry but sweet.

Common in coastal and lowland habitats, in open areas in
forests and at the heads of beaches, Thimbleberry is most
abundant on southeastern Graham Island, where it forms
thickets along the roadside.

Thimbleberry produces flowers in July and the berries are
ripe by early August. Flowers and ripening berries can be
found on the same branches. The berries were traditionally eaten by the Haida, either fresh or dried. In other
areas on the coast, young stalks were peeled and eaten
raw. Thimbleberries are popular today, eaten fresh from
the bush.

Key characteristic: A bushy shrub with large, lax leaves;
large white flowers; dull red, thimble-shaped berries.

Western Thimbleberry, *Rubus parviflorus*. (X 1/2)

ROSACEAE   ROSE FAMILY

Rubus spectabilis Pursh   **Salmonberry**

A bushy, deciduous shrub up to 3 m high, Salmonberry has
small spines on the stems and branches. The leaves are
thin, coarsely toothed and triangular in shape, arranged
in threes, with 1 central leaflet (maximum 6 cm long) and
2 lateral ones. Flowers are solitary, about 3 cm across,
with 5 spreading, rose-coloured petals that are fully
developed before the leaves open. There are numerous
stamens. The fruit is a compound berry, about 17 mm
across, that is shiny, juicy and sweet. Either red or
yellow berries are produced on different bushes.

Salmonberry is present in most lowland habitats on the
Islands except the bogs. It is common along rivers and on
stabilized beach margins and abundant, sometimes
thicket-like, along roads on southern Graham Island and
northern Moresby Island.

Flowers develop as early as mid-March, and the berries
ripen by June. Traditionally, the watery berries were
eaten fresh by the Haida and young stems were peeled and
eaten raw; presently, Salmonberry is still popular as a
fresh fruit.

The red colour of the berry is due to the presence of
anthocyanin pigment. The colour is thought to be con-
trolled by a single gene, with red colour dominant. The
Haida made a distinction between the berry colour forms -
in the Masset dialect, there are different words for the
different coloured berries.

Key characteristics: A bushy shrub with small spines;
leaves in threes; flowers rose-pink with spreading petals;
fruit a yellow or red compound berry.

Salmonberry, *Rubus spectabilis*. (X 1/2)

ROSACEAE   ROSE FAMILY

Spiraea douglasii Hook. ssp. *menziesii*   **Hardhack**
(Hook.) Calder & Taylor

                                        Not illustrated

Hardhack is a thicket-forming deciduous shrub up to 1.5 m
tall. The leaves are oblong, about 5 cm long, with a
serrated apex; the under-surface of the leaf is hairy. The
small rose-coloured flowers are 5-petalled, densely com-
pacted in an elongate terminal cluster. The seeds are
contained in small open capsules.

At the headwaters of the Tlell River, Graham Island
(called "the Pontoons" locally), Hardhack forms large
colonies. Elsewhere on the Islands, the plant is rare.

Key characteristics: Spreading shrub with oblong, serrated
leaves; rosy flowers in apical upright clusters.

SALICACEAE   WILLOW FAMILY

Salix scouleriana Barrett in Hook.   **Scouler's Willow**

Scouler's Willow is a small tree reaching a maximum height
of 5 m; on exposed coasts, it is a much smaller shrub. The
leaves are oblong, narrowing to a point at the base, about
8 cm long with smooth margins. The minute flowers are in
spikes, or catkins, attached laterally to the branches.
The staminate (male) catkin is fuzzy, and Scouler's Willow
is locally called Pussy Willow. The catkins develop before
the leaves expand.

Scouler's Willow is found near the coast on all but the
west side of the Islands; it is never common and only
grows with good light exposure.

There are 5 additional species of Willow on the Islands;
all are extremely rare. **Hooker's Willow** (*Salix hookeriana*)
has only been found on the west coast of Moresby Island
and **Stoloniferous Willow** (*S. stolonifera*) on the west

Scouler's Willow, *Salix scouleriana.* **(X 1/2)**

coast of Graham. **Pacific Willow** (*S. lasiandra*) and **Sitka Willow** (*S. sitchensis*) are trees up to 6 m high found along the shores of large lakes or rivers. **Net-leaved Dwarf Willow** (*S. reticulata* ssp. *glabellicarpa*) is a sub-species of willow endemic to the Queen Charlotte Islands; it is a prostrate shrub found in the alpine.

Key characteristics: A small tree with narrow, smooth-edged leaves; flowers in catkins that develop before the leaves expand; male catkins fuzzy.

SALICACEAE   WILLOW FAMILY

Populus balsamifera L. ssp. *trichocarpa*   **Black Cottonwood**
(Torr. & Gray ex Hook.) Brayshaw

                                         Not illustrated

On the Islands, Black Cottonwood is a tree less than 10 m tall; the bark is deeply furrowed in age. The stiff decid-uous leaves, attached alternately to branches, are roughly triangular in shape and about 10 cm long. Male and female catkins are on different trees; the seeds are released from the catkin along with a fluffy cotton that aids wind-dispersal.

Black Cottonwood has been found only on the shore of Yakoun Lake, Graham Island, where there are scattered trees. Its presence there remains unexplained. Is the stand a remnant of a much wider distribution in the area in the past? Or do these trees represent new immigrants to the Islands?

Key characteristics: Deciduous; deeply furrowed bark; triangular leaves; cotton released from catkins.

90

SOURCES

Calder, J.A. and R.L. Taylor. 1968. Flora of the Queen Charlotte Islands. Part 1. Canada Department of Agriculture, Research Branch, Monograph No. 4, Ottawa.

Clark, L.J. 1976. Wild Flowers of the Pacific Northwest. Evergreen Press Limited, Vancouver.

Griffiths, A.J.F. and F.R. Ganders. 1983. Wildflower Genetics. Flight Press, Vancouver.

Hebda, R.J. and R.W. Mathewes. 1984. Holocene History of Cedar and Native Indian Cultures of the North American Pacific Coast. Science 225:711-713.

Hosie, R.C. 1973. Native Trees of Canada. Department of the Environment, Government of Canada, Ottawa.

Hulten, E. 1968. Flora of Alaska and Neighboring Territories. Stanford University Press, Stanford.

Joyce, C. 1990. Cancer drug found in bark of American tree. New Scientist 1737:20.

Krajina, V.J. 1969. Ecology of forest trees in British Columbia. Ecology of Western North America 2:1-146.

Lyons, C.P. 1952. Trees, Shrubs and Flowers to Know in British Columbia. J.M. Dent & Sons (Canada) Limited, Vancouver.

Scudder, G.E.E. and N. Gessler. 1989. The Outer Shores. Based on the Proceedings of the Queen Charlotte Islands First International Scientific Symposium, University of British Columbia, August 1984. Queen Charlotte Islands Museum Press. Queen Charlotte, British Columbia.

Taylor, R.L. and B. MacBryde. 1977. Vascular Plants of British Columbia. University of British Columbia Press, Vancouver.

Szczawinski, A.F. 1962. The Heather Family (Ericaceae) of British Columbia. British Columbia Provincial Museum Handbook No. 19, Victoria.

Turner, N.J. 1974. Plant taxonomic systems and ethnobotany of three contemporary Indian groups of the Pacific Northwest (Haida, Bella Coola, and Lillooet). Syesis 7 (Supplement 1): 1-104.

Turner, N.J. 1975. Food Plants of British Columbia Indians. Part 1. Coastal Peoples. British Columbia Provincial Museum Handbook No. 34, Victoria.

Turner, N.J. 1978. Food Plants of British Columbia Indians. Part 2. Interior Peoples. British Columbia Provincial Museum Handbook No. 36, Victoria.

Turner, N.J. 1979. Plants in British Columbia Indian Technology. British Columbia Provincial Museum Handbook No. 38, Victoria.

INDEX

98

The plant illustrations are being offered as limited edition prints in their original 23 cm by 30 cm format. Please send queries to the author at Islands Ecological Research, Box 970, Queen Charlotte, British Columbia, V0T 1S0.

Printed in Canada on recycled paper.